CW00417542

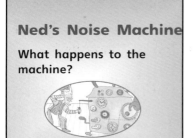

Ned's Noise Machine

What happens to the machine?

What sort of noises do machines make? (*e.g. cars, vacuum cleaners, etc*)

Who can you see in the picture?

What sort of person do you think Ned is? (*wacky inventor*)

Walkthrough

This is the back cover – let's read the blurb together.

'What happens to the machine?'

(Prompt for suggestions.)

Walkthrough

We've thought about the noises that machines we know make.

What sort of noise do you think Ned's noise machine will make?

Now let's read the title together.

Read the names of the author, illustrator and publisher.

1

Walkthrough

Establish the structure of the book by saying, 'The noise Ned's machine is making on this page is 'pip'. How can it go?'

It can go pip.

2

 Observe and Prompt

Word Recognition

- Check the children can read the sight words 'It' and 'go'.
- Check the children are reading 'can', 'pip' and 'pop' using their decoding skills. Can they sound out and blend all through the words?

Walkthrough

Now it goes 'pop'.

How can it go?

It can go pop.

3

Observe and Prompt

Language Comprehension

- Check the children understand what is happening at the beginning of the story.
- Ask the children what noises Ned's Noise Machine makes.
- Check the children have picked up the pattern of the text.

Walkthrough

Now it goes 'tick'.

How can it go?

It can go tick.

4

 Observe and Prompt

Word Recognition

● Check children are reading 'tick' and 'tock' using their
decoding skills. If the children have difficulties with these
words, ask them to identify the initial letter and sound – 't'.
Then model the reading of the words for them.

4

Walkthrough

Then it goes 'tock'.

How can it go?

It can go tock.

5

 Observe and Prompt

Language Comprehension

- Ask the children what noise the machine is making now.
- Ask the children what Ned might be thinking. What might the children in the story be thinking?

What noises do you think it is going to make on this page?

How do you know?

It can go pip, pip, pip.

6

 **Observe and Prompt**

Word Recognition

- Check the children are reading 'pip' and 'tick' using their decoding skills. Can they sound and blend the phonemes through the words?

Walkthrough

What noises do you think it will make now?

What do you think might be about to happen?

It can go tick, tick, tick.

7

 Observe and Prompt

Language Comprehension

- Ask the children what is happening now in the story. What noises is the machine making?

- What do the children think might happen next?

Walkthrough

What big noise do you think the machine makes?

What mark tells you this is a big noise?
(Point out exclamation mark.)

It can go bang!

8

 Observe and Prompt

Word Recognition

- If the children have difficulties with the word 'bang', ask them if they recognise the initial letter and sound – 'b'. Then model the reading of this word for them.

 Observe and Prompt

Language Comprehension

- Check the children understand what has happened at the end of the story.
- Check the children read with expression.
- Check they notice the exclamation mark.